JOHN FORD'S
STAGECOACH
STARRING
JOHN WAYNE

Edited by Richard J. Anobile

A DARIEN HOUSE BOOK

UNIVERSE BOOKS
NEW YORK

ACKNOWLEDGMENTS

I would like to take this opportunity to thank those corporations and individuals who helped to make this book possible.

The rights to produce this book were granted to us by the Lorrimer Publishing Ltd. through the efforts of Mr. Andrew Sinclair. Ms. Nicola Fischer coordinated the gathering of the materials for this project which were supplied to us by Mr. Jackson E. Dube.

Mr. Bob Thomas of Action Magazine was kind enough to grant us permission to reprint John Ford's comments about STAGECOACH.

Alyne Model, George Norris and Jan Kohn of Riverside Film Associates in New York accurately transferred my frame selections to negative material. The blowups were produced at the Vita Print Corp. under the supervision of Mr. Saul Jaffe.

Harry Chester Associates was responsible for the design of this book. And Helen Garfinkle of Darien House kept me sufficiently isolated from the normal office humdrum so as to allow me to thoroughly concentrate on this project.

RICHARD J. ANOBILE

Note to reader:

In keeping as true to the film as possible I have left in lap dissolves and fades where I felt they were necessary. The effect of a lap dissolve to the reader will be the appearance of two seemingly superimposed photos. The purpose here – as it was the director's, is to bridge the time and place gap between two scenes.

You will also notice a fuzziness in some frames. This is due to the fact that every photo is taken from blow-ups of the film itself. All possible means have been taken to insure clarity but inconsistencies in negative quality account for the variations of photo densities you will observe.

A DARIEN HOUSE BOOK

UNIVERSE BOOKS
381 Park Avenue South
New York, N.Y. 10016

Library of Congress Catalog Card Number: 75-4265

First Printing, April 1975.

ISBN 0 87663 220 7

Printed in the United States of America

Introduction

Viewing STAGECOACH today without understanding its significance in the evolution of the film might simply leave the viewer yawning. Especially if it is seen on the tiny screen.

John Ford's STAGECOACH is not just a classic in the annals of Hollywood; it is also a milestone in both the art and science of motion picture production. From it have sprung innumerable other Westerns—including the raw and raunchy "spaghetti-Western" for which Italy became so famous a few years ago.

STAGECOACH, it may be said, revolutionized the western epic by breaking out of the sterile, artificial confines of the Hollywood sound stage. In the beginning, say 1903, Edwin S. Porter shot his THE GREAT TRAIN ROBBERY on location in the wilds of New Jersey. But, as time passed and film-making became more technically sophisticated, directors headed West—and indoors—where virtually all "external conditions" could be controlled. Thus, by 1939, Hollywood had discovered rear-screen projection and put it to good use; second units would head out for the sage brush and record the proper outdoor scenery, which then would be unreeled to serve as background for the sound stage-bound actors. Thus, most Westerns of that period tended to be rather stagey.

But in 1939, John Ford wrote *finis* to this epoch. Not only did he "discover" Monument Valley, he turned it into some sort of private outdoor set that he was to use, time and again, for the next quarter of a century. Into the valley lumbered caravans of trucks brimming with equipment and crews, and for about two months, the STAGECOACH company would work on cue from Mother Nature—often under the most grueling conditions.

But lest I overemphasize the technical aspects of STAGECOACH'S significance, it must be said here and now that the script, more than the setting, is what makes STAGECOACH such a film classic.

Together with filmwriter Dudley Nichols, Ford helped forge a human drama unparalleled in any previous Western. Each character in STAGECOACH is meticulously drawn; each contributes a different perspective of the situation. Indeed, so concisely do Ford and Nichols do their work that by the end of the second reel—about 20 minutes into the film—the audience has such a grasp for the characters that alliances are invariably struck. Even more interesting, from the vantage point of nearly 40 years later, is that for the first time the audience gravitates not necessarily to hero and heroine but to the so-called "little people"—the philosophic but alcoholic doctor (Thomas Mitchell), banished from town along with the prostitute with the heart of gold (Claire Trevor), and, of course, the "Ringo Kid" (John Wayne), a good boy gone wrong.

These characters are balanced against the good but snobbish woman (Louise Platt) and her escort, the town's suave gentleman gambler (John Carradine) and the all-American banker (Berton Churchill) whose flag-waving platitudes seem downright Nixonian and Agnewesque—especially in light of the fact that he's absconding with $50,000 of the bank's deposits.

About the only "neutral" character in the stagecoach is a liquor salesman (Donald Meek), whose dual function in the film seems to be that of keeping Thomas Mitchell sloshed and taking the first Indian arrow at the start of the near-climactic siege. Inevitably, Ford and Nichols also provide us with the archetypal sheriff (Curley, played by George Bancroft) and the screechy stage driver (Buck, played by Andy Devine).

Compared with many other Westerns that have followed STAGECOACH, the Ford-Nichols play seems both dated and hackneyed. Despite our involvement with the characters, after all is said and done, we can almost predict the outcome of the story—so accustomed have we become to this formula. But remember that it started here, with STAGECOACH, and consider also how deliciously satisfying the story actually is, seen in the wake of Watergate: the scorned, dumped-upon characters triumph; the sanctimonious, upstanding, uptight banker is hauled off to the pokey.

THE POSEIDON ADVENTURE, EARTHQUAKE, TOWERING INFERNO, and others in the currently-popular genre of disaster films may come and go, but STAGECOACH may actually be more harrowing in terms of sustained adventure. Nichols' people weren't one-dimensional. Their lines were written to serve almost as background to the external happenings. Ford's camera remains sensitive to all the personality traits of Nichols' characters and their inward and outward struggles in the face of ever-present dangers.

Moreover, Ford wasn't going to play tricks with fancy camera angles and movements. In bringing to life the continuity, Ford was direct and to the point and at times even down-right frugal. When he might have given us the seemingly-obligatory shots of Indians preparing for their attack, he doesn't. Indians are, in fact, spoken of and pointed at throughout the film, but it isn't until they mount their steeds in the next-to-last reel that we get our first glimpse of assembling Indians. Up to that point, the closest we ever came were some shots of distant mountains and ominous smoke signals. I was left with the distinct feeling that all those long shots of the stagecoach snaking its way through the desert were actually through the eyes of an unseen but omnipresent enemy.

But when they do attack, it's pure cinematic wonder. Indians fall two at a time; horses seem to be trampling the cameras and John Wayne (actually veteran stuntman Yakima Canutt) makes his famous leap onto the team of unmanned horses (page 195). Ford literally choreographs this sequence right down to the last bullet. Inside the coach Carradine is preparing to fire that bullet into Platt's skull to spare her the ultimate degradation at the hands of savages. This scene was cleverly set by an earlier scene where the gambler covered the dead body of a woman found at the coach's last stop (page 168).

Traditionally, the attack ought to have signaled the end of the film. But Ford went on to bring us the climactic confrontation between the Ringo Kid and the Plummer brothers. For my part, this is the frosting on the cake. He zeroes in on Luke Plummer (Joseph Rickson) and in so doing quickly establishes both the character and the legend he spins in the town of Lordsburgh. The announcement that the Kid is in town stops Plummer's poker game; tension fills the saloon as both Plummer and the audience brace for the inevitable gun fight.

Now the screen is filled with close-ups of Plummer's straining face as he readies his psyche for the battle (page 216). He downs his whiskey, and we sense Plummer feels trapped; there's no reason for him to take on Ringo. But his public expects him to do so.

His brothers come to his side, and the battle ensues. We hear the shots and, suddenly, Luke Plummer strides back into the saloon. He is expressionless. And then, at the very last moment (when we least expect it), he grimaces and falls over, dead.

This entire sequence is totally understated. A director of lesser stature would have been tempted to add unnecessary embellishments. Even so, Ford doesn't get off scot-free: we see a newspaper editor shouting at his typesetter to prepare a story about the Kid's death (page 240). It may be sheer speculation on my part, but I'd guess that John Ford was probably talked into this needless "footnote."

I am pleased to be able to include John Ford's STAGECOACH in the *Film Classics Library* and it is my hope that this volume will prove both entertaining and utilitarian. This is the most complete record of STAGECOACH in book form. True, sound effects and music are missing but all the dialogue is coupled with over 1200 frame blowups and I feel that such a vivid recreation will force you to literally hear the horses' hooves and the sound of the cavalry's charge.

Directly following these remarks are those of John Ford. They are taken from *Action Magazine* and give an interesting perspective to STAGECOACH. Many of the problems Ford faced in 1939 are constantly faced today by artists and some independent producers. Studio executives have always been a breed trapped by success cycles; it seems to go with the job. Luckily, there are those artists and independent producers who are capable of working within such narrow quarters so that in and amongst the purely commercial fluff masterpieces such as STAGECOACH do emerge.

Richard J. Anobile
New York City
February, 1975

John Ford on Stagecoach

I found the story by reading it in *Collier's*, I think it was. It wasn't too well developed, but the characters were good. "This is a great story," I thought, and I bought it for a small amount — I think it was $2,500.

I tried to sell it to the studios, but nobody was buying. After the studio heads read it, they said to me, "But this is a Western! People don't make Westerns any more!"

"Sure, it's a Western," I said. "But there are great characters in it. What's the difference whether it's played in the West, or wherever?"

I couldn't convince them. Finally I got down to RKO. The president of the company was a gentleman named Joseph P. Kennedy, who happened to be a friend of mine. I went to Joe and told him about the story and how much trouble I had selling it to the studios.

"What's the objection?" he asked me.

"Well, they say it's a *Western*," I said.

"Maybe it's about time they started doing Westerns again," said Kennedy. "I'll tell you what I'll do. I'll send it to the producers at the studio and see what they think."

So he sent it to the so-called producers at RKO — four men who also happened to be close friends of mine. One of them said, "I only do classics" — which was an expression he had learned only recently.

My answer was: "A story is a story, whether it's laid in the West or whether it's *Two Gentlemen from Verona*."

Joe Kennedy couldn't convince his producers. He told me: "I don't know what the hell I'm paying those fellows for. I'm certainly not getting very good pictures from them. I remember when you came to RKO with a story about the Irish Revolution called *The Informer*, and none of those producers were interested in it, either. So the studio sent you across the street to shoot it on one set. That picture gave RKO a lot of prestige. Have you got a script?"

"I'm working on an outline with Dudley Nichols," I said.

Joe Kennedy said he'd like to see it. But meanwhile, I got a call from Walter Wanger, who had one more picture to make under his United Artists contract.

"I understand you've got a good story," Walter said. "What's it called?"

"Stagecoach," I said.

"A Western, huh?" he said.

"Yeah," I said.

"Well, that might be a good idea," he said. "Is it exciting?"

"I think it is," I said.

"Okay, let's talk," he said.

So I sent him the short story and he said, "That's a pretty good story. I'd like to see Gary Cooper play the lead."

I told him I doubted that Coop would want to play in a Western like this one.

"I'd like to have a couple of top stars in it," said Wanger.

"I don't think Gary would fit the part," I said.

"I'm thinking of Gary Cooper and Marlene Dietrich," he said.

"I don't think you can go that high on salary with a picture like this," I said. "This is the kind of picture you have to make for peanuts."

"Have you got anybody in mind?" Wanger asked me.

"Well, there's a boy I know who used to be assistant prop man and bit player for me," I said. "His name was Michael Morrison, but he's making five-day Westerns and he calls himself John Wayne now."

"Do you think he's any good?" he asked.

"Yes, I think so," I said. "And we can get him for peanuts."

"What about the girl?" he said.

"Well, I think Claire Trevor is a helluva actress," I said, "and she fits the part."

"Okay, go ahead and cast the picture," Wanger said, "but I'm leaving for New York. I'll be gone for ten days and when I get back, I'd like you to have the script ready."

So he went off and I assembled a good cast. Besides Wayne and Claire Trevor, I got Thomas Mitchell, Andy Devine, John Carradine. Wanger had a girl under contract, Louise Platt, who fitted into the picture. Then I got that wonderful character actor—what's his name?—oh, yes—Berton Churchill; he played the crooked banker. Donald Meek was the liquor salesman, and George Bancroft played the driver. Good cast.

I did the location scenes first.

I had driven through Monument Valley, and I thought it would be a good place to shoot a Western. I used it for the first time in Stagecoach.

There was a dry lake that was perfect for the Indian attack. We didn't have any camera cars in those days; we just put the camera on an automobile and shot on the run. It was fast. I asked the driver how fast we had gone, and he said 40 to 42 miles per hour. You wouldn't think that horses could go that fast, but they did.

The chase took two days to shoot.

That chase . . . every half-assed critic says, "Why did it go on so long? Why didn't the Indians just shoot the horses?"

I tell them, "If the Indians had done that, they would have stopped the picture."

The real truth is that the Indians were more interested in the horses than in the white men. They fought on foot most of the time, and they needed horses. Besides, they were notoriously bad shots on horseback.

I did about four days on location, and then we went back and finished the picture on the Goldwyn lot. The script was not prolix; there were no long speeches. I shot it pretty much as it was written. Dudley Nichols was on the set at all times, even though he wasn't getting paid for it. If I needed a new line, we'd work it out together.

The shoot-out at the end was something I had done once before with Harry Carey—I had done a lot of silent Westerns with Carey and with Tom Mix, but never a talkie. I used the same idea again in My Darling Clementine.

It went back to what Wyatt Earp had told me. Wyatt was a friend of mine—in fact, I still have his rifle in the corner of my bedroom. He told me: "I'm not a dead shot. I always walked up pretty close to the other fellow before I fired. The legend has it that I killed a lot of people. As a matter of fact, I never killed anybody. I shot people in the shoulder or in the leg, but I never killed them. I left that to my partner, Jones, who was a dead shot."

I made the picture for a good price—$220,000 I think it was. Came in $8,000 under budget. Today you couldn't make that picture for under $10 million.

Duke did okay. He knew his lines, and he did what he was told to do. Of course, I surrounded him with superb actors, and some of the glitter rubbed off on his shoulders. But he's still up there with the best of them. He's goddam good.

After I shot Stagecoach, I worked closely with the cutter. But there wasn't a helluva lot to do. I cut with the camera.

When the picture was put together, Wanger invited a few top people—brilliant brains of the industry, who proceeded to say how they would have done Stagecoach. Sam Goldwyn said, "Walter, you made one mistake: You should have shot it in color. You should start all over again and make it in color." Douglas Fairbanks Sr. said: "The chase is too long."

Then it was shown to the great producers at RKO. One of them said, "It's just a B picture." Another said, "It's all right, but it's still a Western."

Well, of course, the picture went out and hit the jackpot. It started a flood of Westerns, and we've been suffering from them ever since.

Westerns—I never look at them, but I love to make them. Why? Because they're made mostly on location. You're out there in the open, away from the smog and the freeways. You're with a bunch of stunt men who are your friends, and they keep a pitch game going all the time. You eat well—I always insisted on the best possible food on location. You work from dawn until sunset, and you sleep like a baby at night. It's a great life—who wouldn't like it? □

White Scout: These hills are full of Apaches. They've burned every ranch building in sight. He had a brush with 'em last night. Says they're being stirred up by Geronimo.

Capt. Sickels: Geronimo? How do we know he isn't lying?

White Scout: Naw—he's a Cheyenne. They hate Apaches worse than we do.

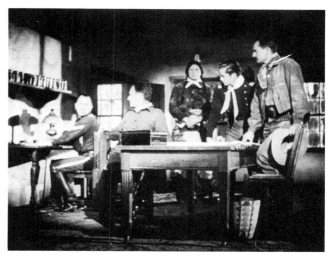

Capt. Sickels: Clear the wire to Lordsburg.

Non-Com: That's Lordsburg now, sir. They seem to have something very urgent to tell you, sir.
Capt. Sickels: Well—what's wrong?

Non-Com: The line went dead, sir.
Capt. Sickels: What've you got there?

Non-Com: Only the first word, sir.

Capt. Sickels: Geronimo!

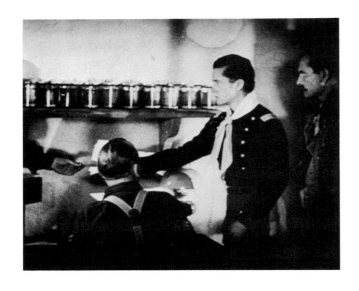 

Buck: Whoa! Whoa! Steady—whoa!

Voices: Well, so long, Buck. Nice trip, Buck? So long, kid . . .
Buck: Well, so-so . . .
Wells Fargo Agent: Howdy, Buck—got that payroll for the mining company?

Buck: Yes, sir, right in the Wells Fargo box.

Buck: Jim, I'll pay you that two bits when I come back.
Jim: Okay—okay—

Buck: Whoa! Get away from those wheels, boys.

Buck: Well, we ran into a little snow up there—wasn't too bad—but you fellows better prepare for a good frost.

Buck: Passengers out for Tonto . . .

Buck: You better get out and stretch your legs.

Buck: I mean your limbs, ma'am. We're going to change horses here.

Lucy: Is there someplace where I can have a cup of tea?
Buck: Well, yes, ma'am, you can get a cup o' coffee at the hotel right across the street there.

Lucy: Thank you, driver.
Buck: You're lookin' a little . . .
Lucy: I'll be all right, thank you.

Buck: Yes, ma'am . . .

Nancy: Why, Lucy Mallory!

Lucy: Nancy!

Lucy: How are you, Capt. Whitney?
Capt. Whitney: Fine, thanks, Mrs. Mallory.

Nancy: Why whatever are you doing in Arizona?

Lucy: I'm joining Richard in Lordsburg. He's there with his troops.

Capt. Whitney: He's a lot nearer than that, Mrs. Mallory. He's been ordered to Dry Fork.

Nancy: Why that's the next stop for the stagecoach. You'll be with your husband in a few hours.

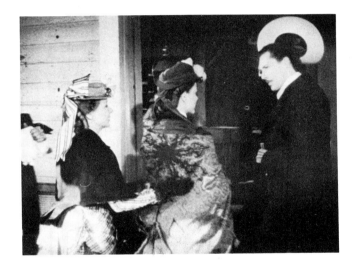

Nancy: Oh, I'm so glad to see you, Lucy.

Nancy: Sit down, darling, and have a cup of coffee. You must be tired from that long trip.
Lucy: Who is that gentleman?

Capt. Whitney: Hardly a gentleman, Mrs. Mallory.
Nancy: I should think not! He's a notorious gambler.

Buck: Hello, Mink—hidy Frank.

Buck: . . . Well, Marshal, I'm lookin' for my shotgun guard. Is he here?

Curly: Out with a posse, Buck—tryin' to ketch the Ringo Kid.

Buck: Ringo! I thought Ringo was in the pen.
Curly: He was.

Buck: Busted out? Well, good for him!

First Deputy: It's my guess the Kid's aimin' to get even with them Plummer boys.
Second Deputy: It was their testimony sent him to the penitentiary.

Buck: Well, all I got to say is he better keep away from that there Luke Plummer. Why, gosh, Luke's run all of Ringo's friends out of Lordsburg.

Buck: Why the last trip there I seen him hit a rancher on the head with the barrel of his gun and—well, he just laid it wide open like a butchered steer.

Curly: You seen Luke Plummer in Lordsburg?

Buck: Yessirree.

Curly: Huh.

Curly: You boys take care of the office for a couple-a days.

Curly: I'm goin' to Lordsburg with Buck. Goin' to ride shot-gun.

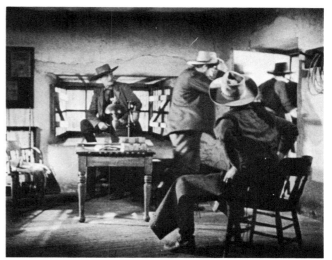

Buck: Oh, gosh, if I could just learn to keep my big mouth shut.

Agent: Here's the payroll, Mr. Gatewood.

Gatewood: You know, ever since I opened this bank I've been trying to tell those people to deposit their payrolls six months in advance. It's good, sound business.

Agent: It's good business for you, Mr. Gatewood.

Gatewood: Well, there's your receipt. Fifty thousand dollars.

Gatewood: And remember this—what's good for the banks is good for the country.

Doc Boone: Now—now, now, my dear lady—

Landlady: Good riddance to bad rubbish.

Landlady: Get out and stay out. I'm keeping your trunk because you ain't paid your rent.

Doc Boone: "Is this the face that wrecked a thousand ships —

Doc Boone: And burned the towerless tops of Ilium?"

24

Doc Boone: Farewell, fair Helen.

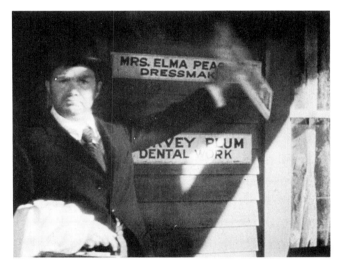

Dallas: Doc, Doc!

Dallas: Can they make me leave town when I don't want to go?

Dallas: Do I have to go?
Doc Boone: Sh . . .

Sheriff: Now, Dallas, don't you go makin' no fuss.

Dallas: Do I have to go, Doc? Just because they say so?
Sheriff: Now, Dallas, I've got my orders. Don't blame these ladies. It ain't them.

Doc Boone: We're the victims of a foul disease called social prejudice, my child.

Dallas: It is them. Doc, haven't I any right to live? What have I done?

Doc Boone: These dear ladies of the Law and Order League are scouring out the dregs of the town. . . . Come on—be a proud, glorified dreg like me.

Sheriff: You get going, Doc—you're drunk.

Landlady: Huh! Two of a kind—just two of a kind.

Doc Boone: Take my arm, Madame la Comtesse. The tumbril awaits. To the guillotine!

Landlady: Wait till I get my badge, girls—I'll join you.

27

Peacock: If ever you go East, brother, come out to our house for dinner. No one in Kansas City, Kansas, sets a better table than my dear wife, Violet.

Doc Boone: Jerry—
Bartender: Yes, Doc . . .

Doc Boone: Jerry, I will admit as one man to another, that economically I haven't been of much value to you. But— suppose you could put one on credit?

Bartender: If talk was money, Doc, you'd be the best customer I got.

Doc Boone: I'm leaving town, Jerry.
Bartender: Honest?
Doc Boone: Yes, old friend and—I thought you might out of memory of our many happy . . .

Bartender: All right, Doc—just this one.

Doc Boone: Thank you, Jerry.

Bartender: Here's a man goin' on the stagecoach with you. He's an Easterner, from Kansas City, Missouri.

Peacock: Kansas City, Kansas, brother.

Doc Boone: Your health, Reverend.

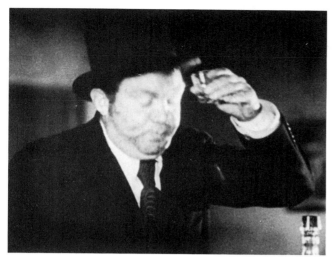

Peacock: I'm not a clergyman. My name is Peacock. I'm a . . .

Bartender: He's a whiskey drummer.

Doc Boone: What? Well, well—how are you, Mr. Haycock.

Peacock: Peacock!

Doc Boone: Don't tell me, sir—I know—I know—a familiar name—an honored name! I never forget a face or a friend.

Doc Boone: Samples? . . .

Doc Boone: Hm . . .

Doc Boone: . . . ah!

Doc Boone: Rye!

Buck: Well—Brownie—lookee here—Giddyap—Whoa! Back up there—

Mrs. Gatewood: I want five dollars, Henry.

Gatewood: Certainly, my dear, certainly. Well, what is it to be this time, my dear—a new . . .

Mrs. Gatewood: I want to pay the butcher. Dinner's at twelve o'clock.
Gatewood: Don't worry, my dear—I'll be there.

Mrs. Gatewood: I've invited the làdies of the Law and Order League.

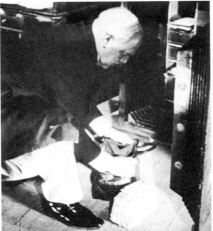

Buck: All aboard for Dry Fork, Apache Wells, Lee's Ferry and Lordsburg.

Doc Boone: I'll take that, Dallas.
Dallas: Oh—thanks.

Sheriff: In you go, Dallas—and a pleasant voyage!

 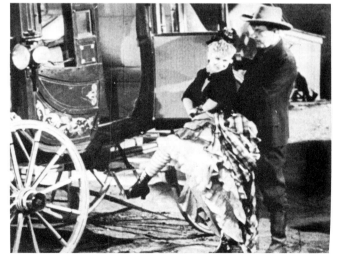

Man: Here's your baggage, Doc.

Doc: Thank you—thank you, my friend. Curly, here's my shingle—carry it with honor.

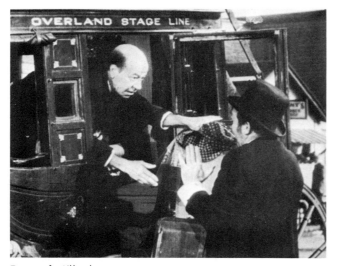

Peacock: I'll take my case . . .

Doc: No trouble—no trouble at all. Why, I can carry it on my lap . . .

Mrs. Gatewood: Mrs. Whitney, you're not going to let your friend travel with that creature!

Mrs. Whitney: She's right, dear. Besides, you're not well enough to travel.

Lucy: It's only a few hours, Nancy. I'm quite all right.
Mrs. Whitney: But you shouldn't travel a step without a doctor.
Lucy: There is a doctor, dear. The driver told me.

Mrs. Gatewood: Doctor! Doc Boone?

Mrs. Gatewood: Why he couldn't doctor a horse.

Nancy: Lucy, darling—you must take care of yourself—try . . .
Buck: Lady folks ride facin' forward, please.

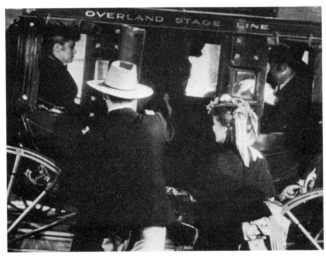

Capt. Whitney: Pleasant journey, Mrs. Mallory.
Lucy: Thank you—goodbye.

Nancy: Goodbye.

Doc: Goodbye.

Hatfield: Like an angel in a jungle—a very wild jungle.

Cowboy: What you doin', Hatfield? Talkin' to yourself?

Hatfield: You wouldn't understand, cowboy.

Hatfield: You've never seen an angel. Nor a gentlewoman—

Hatfield: Nor a great lady. . .

Hatfield: I raise, gentlemen.

Voices: Well, so long, Buck—So long, Curly—Nice trip, boys—

Curly: Wait a minute—hold it!

Lt. Blanchard: Capt. Sickels asks if you will deliver this dispatch in Lordsburg the moment you arrive. The telegraph line has been cut.
Curly: Sure.

Lt. Blanchard: We're going with you as far as the noon station at Dry Fork. There'll be a troop of cavalry there and they'll take you on to Apache Wells.

Lt. Blanchard: From Apache Wells you'll have another escort of soldiers into Lordsburg. But you must warn your passengers that they travel at their own risk.

Curly: At their own risk? Well, what's the trouble, Lieutenant?
Lt. Blanchard: Geronimo!

Buck: Geronimo! Well, then I ain't goin' . . .
Curly: Will you sit down!

Lt. Blanchard: Of course, the Army has no authority over you gentlemen. If you think it unsafe to make the trip . . .
Curly: This stage is going to Lordsburg.

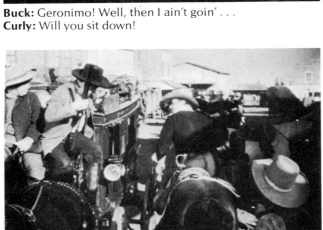

Curly: If you think it ain't safe to ride along with us, I figure we can get there without you soldier-boys.

Lt. Blanchard: I have my orders, sir, and I always obey orders.
Buck: Oh . . .

Curly: Did you all hear what the lieutenant said?

Lucy: Yes, we heard.

Curly: Well, me and Buck are takin' this coach through, passengers or not. Now whoever wants to get out can get out.

Doc: Courage —courage, Reverend.

Doc: Ladies first.
Curly: How about you, Dallas?

Dallas: What are you trying to do— scare somebody? They got me in here —now let 'em try to put me out.

Dallas: There are worse things than Apaches.

Curly: If you'll take my advice ma'am, you won't take this trip.

Lucy: My husband is with his troops in Dry Fork. If he's in danger, I want to be with him.

Peacock: Well, you see, brother, I have a wife and five children—you see—

Doc: Then you're a man. By all the Powers that be, Reverend, you're a man.

Curly: All right, folks . . .

Hatfield: Marshal, room for one more?

Hatfield: I'm offering my protection to this lady.

Hatfield: I can shoot fairly straight if there is need for it.
Curly: That's been proved too many times, Hatfield. All right, get in. We're late.

Hatfield: Tell them to move over, sir.

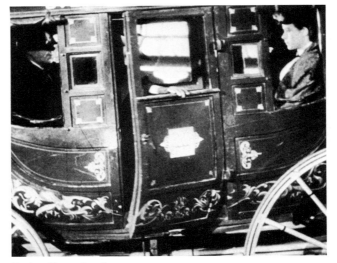

Curly: Close the door . . .

Doc: Goodbye, ladies.

Buck: Oh—Curly . . .

Curly: Get going.

Buck: Bessie, Bonnie—Bill . . .

45

Buck: Whoa—whoa . . .
Gatewood: Room for another passenger?

Buck: Sure is, Mr. Gatewood. Goin' to Lordsburg?
Gatewood: That's right. Just got a telegram—had to stop and pack this bag.

Buck: Hi, Bessie—hi there, Bonnie—Blackie—Bill—Ho!

Buck: Bess—Bonnie—Queenie—steady girl—git alang—Well, if they's anything I don't like it's drivin' a stagecoach through Apache country.

Curly: Funny ketchin' Gatewood outside of town that way.

Buck: I just took this job ten years ago so I could get enough money to marry my Mexican girl, Juliette—I been workin' hard at it ever since . . . Bonnie get over. Whoa! . .

Curly: At marriage?
Buck: Certainly. My wife's got more relations than anyone you ever did see. I bet I'm feedin' half the state of Chihuahua . . .

Curly: Don't it seem funny to you about Gatewood?

48

Buck: Yeah.—And what do I get to eat when I'm home in Lordsburg? Nothing but frijole beans—that's all—nothin' but beans, beans, beans . . .

Buck: Bessie—Bonnie—Blackie—now get alang . . .

Gatewood: Excuse me, ladies—er—

Gatewood: Close quarters—er—warm today.

Doc: Your wife made it warm for me, Gatewood. She was chairman of our farewell committee.

Gatewood: Hm—hm —

Gatewood: Fine looking bunch of soldier-boys back there. It always gives me great pride in my country when I see such fine young men in the U.S. Army.

Gatewood: Anybody know where they're going?

Peacock: Brother, aren't you aware of what's happened?
Gatewood: Happened? I—I don't follow you, Reverend.
Peacock: I'm not a clergyman—I'm . . .

Doc: My friend is a whiskey drummer.

Doc: We're all going to be scalped, Gatewood. Massacred in one fell swoop. That's why the soldiers are with us.

Gatewood: He's joking, of course.

Peacock: Oh, no, he's not. Oh, dear, no. I wish he were.

Doc: It's that old Apache butcher, Geronimo.

Doc: Geronimo—nice name for a butcher. He's jumped the reservation—he's on the warpath.

Gatewood: Geronimo? Why weren't the passengers notified? Why wasn't I told?

Doc: We were told, Gatewood. Weren't you told when you got that message from Lordsburg?

Gatewood: Oh, yes—yes—of course—I forgot . . .

Buck: Steady now—string out ←Sweetheart! Now, doggone it, they're bringin' up her grandfather all the way from Mexico to live with us.
Curly: I can't figure out how he got that message.
Buck: Who, her grandfather?

Curly: No, Gatewood.
Buck: Sweetheart!
Curly: Said he got a message.
Buck: Sweetheart!
Curly: The telegraph line ain't workin'.
Buck: Sweetheart!

Ringo: Hold it.

Buck: Whoa—steady! Whoa! Hey, look—it's Ringo.

Curly: Yeah . . . Hello, Kid.

Ringo: Hello, Curly.

Ringo: Hiya, Buck—how's your folks?

Buck: Oh, just fine, Ringo, except my grandfather came up . . .
Curly: Shut up!

Ringo: Didn't expect you to be ridin' shotgun on this run, Marshal. Goin' to Lordsburg?
Curly: I figured you'd be there by this time.

Ringo: Nope—lame horse. Well, it looks like you've got another passenger.
Curly: Yeah . . . I'll take the Winchester.

Ringo: You may need me and this Winchester, Curly. I saw a ranch house burnin' last night.

Curly: You don't understand, Kid. You're under arrest.
Ringo: Curly—

Lt. Blanchard: Everything all right, Marshal?
Curly: All right, Lieutenant.

Ringo: Hope I ain't crowdin' you folks none.
Peacock: Oh, no . . . the more the merrier.

Buck: Bonnie—Bessie—Blackie—

Buck: Ain't Ringo a fine boy?
Curly: I think so.
Buck: Hey, you're just smarter'n a trade rat. You knew all the time he was goin' to Lordsburg. Hey—reckon what he meant he saw ranch houses burnin'?

Curly: Apaches.
Buck: Oh—Apaches!

Gatewood: So you're the notorious Ringo Kid.

Ringo: My friends just call me Ringo. Nickname I had as a kid. Right name's Henry.

Doc: Seems to me I knew your family, Henry.

Doc: Didn't I fix your arm once when you were, oh—bucked off a horse?
Ringo: Are you Doc Boone?

Doc: I certainly am. Now let's see—I'd just been honorably discharged from the Union Army, after the War of the Rebellion.

Hatfield: You mean the war for the Southern Confederacy, suh.

Doc: I mean nothing of the kind, sir.

Ringo: That was my kid brother broke his arm. You did a good job, Doc, even if you was drunk.

Doc: Thank you, son. Professional compliments are always pleasing.
Peacock: Yes, they are.
Doc: What happened to that boy whose arm I fixed?

Ringo: He was murdered.

Hatfield: Put out that cigar . . . You're annoying this lady.

Doc: Excuse me, madam. Being so partial to the weed myself,

Doc: I sometimes forget that it disagrees with others.

Hatfield: A gentleman doesn't smoke in the presence of a lady.

Doc: Three weeks ago I took a bullet out of a man who was shot by a gentleman. The bullet was in his back.

Hatfield: You mean to insinuate . . .

Ringo: Sit down, mister—

Ringo: Doc don't mean no harm.

Buck: Be careful of Bessie up there now—Take it easy—
hold it steady, girl—steady—hold it . . .

Doc: Well, if it isn't my old friend, Sergeant Billy Pickett! How are you, Billy?
Mrs. Pickett: He's fine, Doc, and mighty glad to see you. Great heavens to Betsy, we didn't figure on no stagecoach comin' through, with them Apaches raisin' Cain. I was jest tellin' Billy to hitch up the buckboard so we could take the young un's into . . .

Gatewood: Just a minute . . . you mean to say there are no troops at this station?

Mrs. Pickett: Ain't no soldiers here but what you see. Is there, Billy?

Lucy: But my husband, Captain Mallory! I was told he was here.
Mrs. Pickett: He was, dearie—got orders night afore last to join the soldiers at Apache Wells.

Buck: Well, that means we got to turn back.

Gatewood: I can't go back.
See here, driver, this stage has started for Lordsburg and it's your duty to get us there. And it's your duty, young man, to come along with us.
Lt. Blanchard: It's my duty, Mr. Gatewood, to obey orders. I'm sorry, sir.

Buck: Oh, well—if you soldiers go back, Lieutenant, it means we all gotta go back.

Lt. Blanchard: My orders are that I am to return from Dry Fork.

Ringo: I think we can get through all right, Curly.

Buck: Don't egg him on like that, Kid. I'm drivin' this outfit and if the soldiers go back so am I.

Gatewood: I call this desertion of duty, young man. I'll take it up with your superior officers. And if necessary I'll take it up with Washington.
Lt. Blanchard: That's your privilege, sir. But if you make any trouble here I'll have to put you under restraint.

Gatewood: Now don't lose your temper, don't lose your temper.

Curly: I'll tell you how we'll settle it. We'll take a vote. Inside everybody. Come on, Buck.

Buck: Oh, Curly, I don't want to . . .

Mrs. Pickett: Now you girls set down and I'll get you somethin' to eat.

Curly: Now, folks, if we push on we can be in Apache Wells by sundown. Soldiers there will give us an escort as far as the ferry, and then it's only a hoot and a holler into Lordsburg.
Buck: Well . . .

Curly: We got four men can handle firearms — five with you, Ringo.

Curly: Doc can shoot, it sober.

Doc: I can shoot—I can shoot . . .

Curly: Now, Mrs. Mallory, I—I ain't goin' to put a lady in danger without she votes for it.

Lucy: I've traveled all the way here from Virginia. I'm determined to get to my husband. I won't be separated any longer.

Curly: What's your vote, mister?

Ringo: Where's your manners, Curly? Ain't you gonna ask the other lady first?

Curly: Well, what do you say?

Dallas: What difference does it make? It doesn't matter.

Gatewood: I vote that we go on. I demand it. I'm standing on my legal rights!

Curly: What do you say, Hatfield?

Hatfield: Lordsburg!

Curly: Four! You, Doc?

Doc: I am not only a philosopher, sir, I'm a fatalist.

Doc: Somewhere, sometime there may be the right bullet or the wrong bottle waiting for Josiah Boone. Why worry when or where?

Curly: Yes or no?
Doc: Having that philosophy, sir, I have always courted danger.

Doc: During the late war—when I had the honor to serve the Union under our great President, Abraham Lincoln, ah—

Doc: And General Phil Sheridan . . .

Doc: I fought 'midst shot and shell and the cannons' roar . . .

Curly: DO YOU WANT TO GO BACK OR NOT?

Doc: NO! . . . I want another drink.

Curly: That's five. How about you, Mr. Hancock?
Peacock: Peacock . . .

Peacock: I—I'd like to go on, Brother, I want to reach the bosom of my dear family in Kansas City, Kansas, as quickly as possible—but I may never reach that bosom if we go on —so—under the circumstances—I—you understand, Brother—I think it best we go back with the bosoms—I mean with the soldiers . . .

Curly: One against. Well, Buck?
Buck: I . . .
Curly: Buck says aye. That's six . . .

Curly: I'm votin' your proxy, Kid. You go with me.

Ringo: Ain't nothin' keepin' me out of Lordsburg, Curly.
Curly: There sure ain't.

Curly: Well, folks, that settles it. We're going through. Set down folks and eat your grub.

Curly: Come on, Buck—we'll change them horses.

Buck: Aw, Curly, ain't we gonna eat?
Curly: We'll eat later.
Buck: Oh . . .

Mrs. Pickett: Food on the table, folks—set down and eat. You got a long ride ahead of you . . .

Mrs. Pickett: You ain't drinkin', Billy?

Ringo: Set down here, ma'am.

Dallas: Thanks.

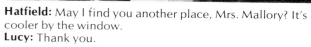

Hatfield: May I find you another place, Mrs. Mallory? It's cooler by the window.
Lucy: Thank you.

Ringo: Looks like I got the plague, don't it.
Dallas: No—it's not you.

Ringo: Well, I guess you can't break out of prison and into society in the same week.

Dallas: Please—please!

Hatfield: You're ill, Mrs. Mallory?

Lucy: No—it's just that I—I'll be all right. You've been very kind . . . why?

Hatfield: In the world I live in one doesn't often meet a lady, Mrs. Mallory.

Lucy: Have you ever been in Virginia?

Hatfield: I was in your father's regiment.

Lucy: I should remember your name. You're Mr. Hatfield?

Hatfield: That's what I'm called—yes.

Dallas: Why do you look at me like that?
Ringo: Just tryin' to remember. Ain't I seen you someplace before, ma'am?

Dallas: No! No, you haven't.

Ringo: Hm—I wish I had though.

Dallas: I know you—I mean I know who you are. I guess everybody in the Territory does.

Ringo: Yep—well I used to be a good cowhand—but— things happened . . .

Dallas: Yeah—that's it—things happen. Now they'll take you back to prison.
Ringo: Not till I finish a job—in Lordsburg.

Dallas: But you can't—you're going there as a prisoner.

Buck: All aboard for Apache Wells . . . Lee's Ferry . . . and . . .

Curly: All right, folks, the horses are ready. We'd better get going . . .

Buck: . . . and Lordsburg—maybe.

Curly: Let's get going. All right, Kid, get going.

Curly: Mrs. Pickett, tell Billy the buckboard's ready . . .
Mrs. Pickett: All right, Marshal, we're ready.
Lt. Blanchard: I'll say goodbye now, Mrs. Mallory, and my compliments to your husband.

Curly: Come on—let's get going.
Peacock: I still feel that we ought to go back with the soldiers.

Buck: Bridesmaid! — Baby! Whoa!

Buck: What'd you say?
Curly: Nothin'.
Buck: Well, why don't you say somethin'? A feller gets nervous settin' here like a dummy with nothing to do but think about those Indians.

Curly: You say somethin'. You been setting here all day talkin' without makin' any sense.

Buck: All right, I'll say somethin' that makes sense—why don't you let 'em shoot it out?
Curly: Let who?

Buck: Luke Plummer and the Kid. There'd be a lot more peace in this Territory if Luke Plummer were so full o' lead he couldn't hold his liquor.
Curly: I ain't sayin' I don't share your sentiments, Buck, but you're a born fool.
Buck: I know it.

Curly: First place, Luke would kill the Kid in a gunfight. In the second place if Luke did get shot he's got two brothers jest as ornery as he is. Nope—the only safe place for Ringo is in the pen and I aim to get him there all in one piece.

Buck: Well, I'll be doggoned if I didn't do you an injury, Curly. I figured you was after the reward.

Curly: Reward? Why the Kid's old man and me was friends—we used to punch cattle together . . . Besides, I could use that five hundred in gold.

Buck: Bridesmaid!

Buck: Steady!

Gatewood: I can't get over the impertinence of that young lieutenant! I'll make it warm for that shavetail. I'll report him to Washington.

Gatewood: We pay taxes to the government and what do we get? Not even protection from the Army.

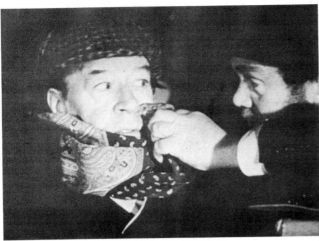

Gatewood: I don't know what the government's coming to! Instead of protecting business men, it's poking its nose into business.

Gatewood: Hm . . . why they're talking now about having bank examiners . . . as if we bankers don't know how to run our own banks.

Gatewood: —I actually had a letter from some popinjay official saying they were going to inspect my books!

Gatewood: I have a slogan, gentlemen, that should be emblazoned on every newspaper in the country. America for Americans! The government must not meddle with business!

Gatewood: Reduce taxes! Our national debt is something shocking—over one billion dollars a year!

Gatewood: . . . What the country needs is a business man for president!

Doc: What the country needs is more fuddle.
Peacock: What?
Doc: Fuddle!

Gatewood: You're drunk.

Doc: I'm happy, Gatewood.

Doc: Boo!

Curly: How come you're takin' this road? — It's gonna be cold up there.

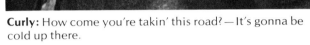

Buck: I'm usin' my head. Those breech-clout Apaches don't like snow.

Dallas: Maybe you'd like to sit next to me? You could put your head on my shoulder.

Lucy: No, thank you.

Hatfield: How are you feeling, Mrs. Mallory?

Lucy: Is there any water?

Hatfield: Driver, canteen, please . . .

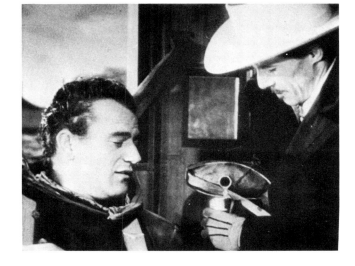

Hatfield: Just a minute, Mrs. Mallory.

Lucy: Haven't I seen this crest before? Isn't this from Greentield Manor?

Hatfield: I wouldn't know, Mrs. Mallory. I won this cup on a wager.

Ringo: How about the other lady?

Dallas: Thanks.

Ringo: Sorry — no silver cups.

Dallas: This is fine.

Gatewood: No.

98

Peacock: Please, doctor . . .

Buck: Yow . . . yow . . .

Buck: Whoa—steady—whoa—steady girl! . . .

Buck: Howdy, Chris. Seven hours from Dry Fork. Pretty fast driving, amigo!

Curly: Get the folks a bite to eat, Chris, while we change horses. We're pushin' right on to Lordsburg.
Chris: You come without soldiers?

Buck: Oh, we wasn't scared.

Buck: We didn't see one Apache, did we, Curly?
Curly: Where's the cavalry, Chris?
Buck: Yeah, where is the soldiers?

Chris: There ain't no soldiers.

Buck: Huh?
Chris: Soldiers have gone.

Lucy: Where's Captain Mallory? Where's my husband? Where is he?

Chris: You his wife—I think?
Lucy: Yes, where is he? Did he go with his men?

Chris: Si, senora. Leetle—what you call it—scrimmage—with the Apaches last night. Soldiers take Captain Mallory to Lordsburg—I think he get hurt, maybe.

Lucy: Badly?

Chris: Si, senora—I think so.

Dallas: Mrs. Mallory—I'm awfully sorry—if there's anything I could . . .
Lucy: I'm quite all right, thank you.

Hatfield: Marshal, come here, quickly.

Dallas: Come on, Doc.

Ringo: Let's go, Doc.
Peacock: Poor woman, I wonder if . . .

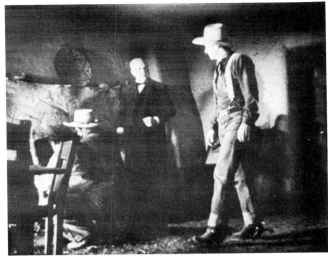

Gatewood: A sick woman on our hands! That's all we
needed.
Buck: I—I feel kinda sick myself.
Gatewood: We're in a fine fix, my friends. It's a fine
country we're living in. The Army has no right to leave a
public place like this undefended.

Ringo: Looks to me like the Army's got its hands pretty
full, mister.

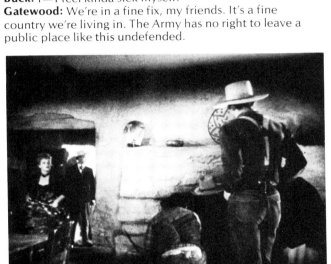

Dallas: Have you a wife?
Chris: Si, senora—I think.
Dallas: Call her.
Chris: YAKIMA—Yakima!

Dallas: Ringo, go into the kitchen, and **get** hot water—lots
of it, please.
Ringo: Yes, ma'am.

Ringo: Hey, Chris—Done la cocima.
Chris: A qui esta, Keed.

Hatfield: A fine member of the medical profession!
Drunken beast!

Doc: Coffee—give me coffee—black coffee—lots of it . . .
More—more . . .

Curly: That's four, Doc—
Doc: More—blacker—stronger . . .

Curly: It'll come out of your ears, Doc.
Doc: Keep 'er comin', Curly.

Curly: All right, Doc . . . Now drink it down—drink it down—get it down—you'll feel better—

Curly: All right, Doc?

Hatfield: Isn't that drunken swine sober yet?
Curly: He's doing the best he can.
Hatfield: Well, hurry.

Ringo: Tin horn . . .

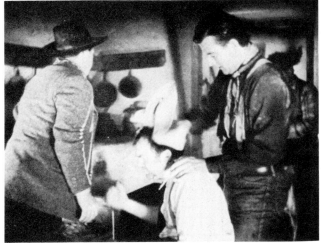

Curly: Keep the fire burning, Chris, and see there's plenty of hot water.

Peacock: SAVAGE!

Chris: That's my wife—my squaw—Yakima.

Peacock: But she—she's a savage.

Chris: Si, Senor—she's leetle bit savage, I think.

Chris: *Va a la cocina—rapido—traies algunas agua caliente!*

Gatewood: There's something funny about this. That woman's an Apache!

Chris: Sure, she one of Geronimo's people—I think. Maybe not so bad to have Apache wife, eh—Apaches don't bother me—I think.

Curly: All right, Doc?

Doc: All right — all right, Dallas . . .

Yakima: *Al pensar en ti*
Tierra en que naci

Yakima: *Que nostalgia siente mi corazon*
En mi soledad

Yakima: *Con este cantar*
Siento alivio y consuelo en mi dolor.

Yakima: *Ahora, hombres vaya!?*

Yakima: *Las notas tristes de esta cancion*

Yakima: *Me traen recuerdos de aquel amor*

Yakima: *Al pensar en el*
Vuelve a renacer

Yakima: *La alegria en mi triste corazon.*

Curly: Ringo!

Buck: It's them vaqueros! They've run away.

Curly: Yeah—with the spare horses.

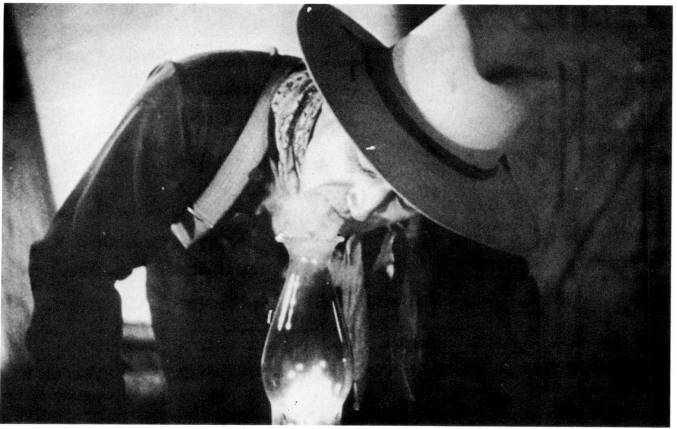

Buck: Them coyotes gimme the creeps. They sound—
well—it sounds just like a baby . . .

Buck: Black eight.

 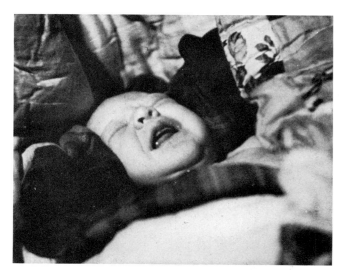

Buck: It's a baby—

Dallas: It's a little girl.

Buck: It's a little girl. Well—I'll be
doggoned. Why didn't someone tell me?

Hatfield: How is Mrs. Mallory?

Dallas: She's going to be all right.

Buck: Well, I'll be doggoned. Did you know? . . . Well,
I'll be doggoned.

Peacock: Don't do that.

125

Peacock: Dr. Boone!

Curly: Come on, boys—three cheers for old Doc Boone!

All: HIP—HIP—
Peacock: Quiet!

Buck: Well, we oughta . . .
Peacock: Quiet—Mrs. Mallory . . .

Curly : Oh!

Chris: Keed—I know why you go to Lordsburg. I like you—I know your Pop—he wuz good friend of mine. If you know who's there you stay away—I think.

Ringo: Hm—you mean Luke Plummer?
Chris: Luke—Ike—and Hank—all three together—I saw them.

Ringo: Sure of that, Chris?
Chris: Si—sure—I tell you the truth—I know . . .

Ringo: Thanks. That's all I wanted to know.
Chris: You crazy if you go. I think you stay away, Keed. Three against one is no good.

Ringo: You oughtn't to go too far, Miss Dallas. Apaches like to sneak up and pick off strays . . .

Ringo: You visiting in Lordsburg?
Dallas: No, I—I have friends there, and maybe I can find work . . .

Ringo: I aim to—in Lordsburg.
Dallas: Why Lordsburg? Why don't you make for the Border now?

Dallas: I lost mine when I was a kid. There was a massacre in Superstition Mountain.
Ringo: That's tough—especially on a girl.

Dallas: Say, look, Kid, why don't you try to escape? Why don't you get away?

Ringo: My father and brother were shot down by the Plummer boys. I guess you don't know how it feels to lose your own folks that way.

Dallas: Well, you gotta live, no matter what happens.

Ringo: Yeah, that's it . . . Look, Miss Dallas—you got no folks—neither have I—well, maybe I'm taking a lot for granted, but I watched you with that baby—that other woman's baby—you looked . . . well . . . well, I still got a ranch across the Border—it's a nice place—a real nice place—trees—grass—water—

Ringo: there's a cabin half built. A man could live there—and a woman. Will you go?

Dallas: But you don't know me. You don't know who I am.

131

Ringo: I know all I want to know—will you go?

Dallas: Oh, don't talk like that.

Curly: What you doin' out here, Kid?
Stick close to the reservation.

Chris: Curly! Oh—Curly! Oh—Curly! Curly!

Curly: What's wrong, Chris?
Chris: My wife, Yakima—she run away. When I wake up she's—gone.
Curly: The way you come bustin' in here . . .

Ringo: Oh . . .
Curly: Excuse me, Kid—

Curly: You'd think we was bein' attacked. You can find another wife, Chris.

Chris: Sure I find another wife! But she take my rifle and my horse! I never sell her—I love her so much. I beat her wid de whip—and she never get tired!

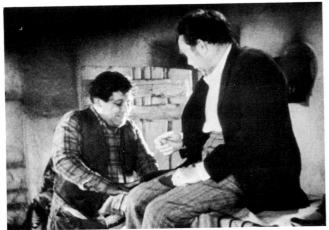

Doc: Your wife?
Chris: No—my horse! I can find another wife easy, yes—but not a horse like that. Yakima, she bad woman. Yakima, she bad woman.

Gatewood: I knew that woman was a thief.

Curly: What's the matter with you, Gatewood?

Gatewood: My valise! Where's my valise? Which one of you's got it?

Buck: Here. I been usin' it for a pillow. I didn't think you would mind.

Gatewood: I told you to keep your hands
off my things!
Buck: Yes, sir . . .

Buck: If that squaw of yours finds some Apaches and brings 'em back here . . .
Chris: My wife's people they won't bother me—I think.
Buck: They bother me, I think.

Doc: Chris, is this bar open?

Chris: Sure—all time . . . senor, si.

Chris: Here you are, Doc.

Gatewood: Well, what are we wasting time for? Let's make a break for it.

Hatfield: We've got a sick woman to think of.

Gatewood: Do you want to stay here and be butchered, with the rest of us?
Hatfield: Why don't you ever think of someone else in your fat, worthless life?
Gatewood: Do you realize . . .

Curly: Easy—easy—quiet, boys, quiet—we ain't been butchered yet. But you're right—we'd better get goin' for Lordsburg as soon as we can.

Ringo: Might be a good idea, Curly, if Doc took a look at his patient.

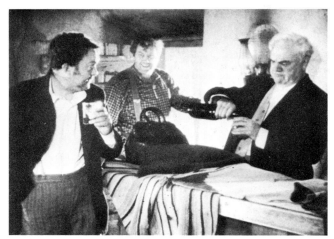

Buck: Yeah, and Little Coyote.
Gatewood: Won't you join me, Doc?

Doc: No thanks.

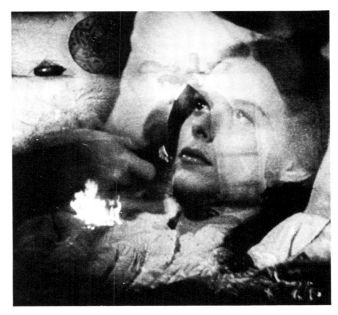

Doc: Good morning.

Doc: Well, you're looking pretty chipper.

Doc: You're up early, Dallas.

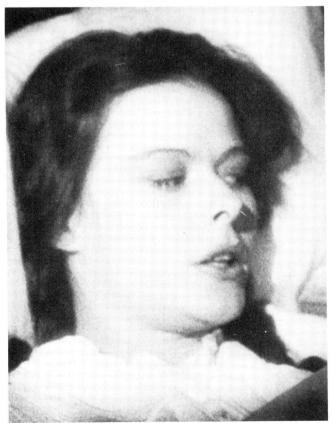

Lucy: She didn't go to bed, Doctor. I'm afraid she sat up all night, while I slept.

Dallas: Oh, I slept a lot in the chair . . . Well, anyway, it was nice to stay awake and hold the baby.

141

Doc: Hm—

Doc: We've got to get you to Lordsburg, Little Coyote.

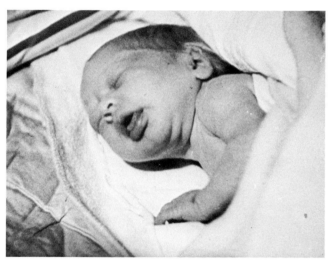

Doc: That's what the boys christened her last night from the way she squalled. Little Coyote . . .

Doc: How do you feel?
Lucy: Fine, thank you. A little tired—Doctor, do you think my husband . . .

Doc: Never mind him! The best medicine he can have is to see you two safe and sound. You just make up your mind you're going to get there.

Lucy: I have made up my mind.
Doc: That's the stuff.
Lucy: I am going to get there.
Doc: You need strength, so get all the rest you can.

Doc: Dallas, do you suppose you can fix up some broth?
Lucy: She has already.

Doc: Good! How about making some coffee for the boys?

Doc: Now you get some sleep, Mrs. Mallory . . .

Doc: And don't look so proud. I've brought hundreds of those little fellows into the world—once upon a time—

Doc: And each new one was always the prettiest.

Dallas: Doc,

Dallas: Ringo asked me to marry him. Is that wrong—for a girl like me? If a man and woman love each other.

Dallas: It's all right, ain't it, Doc?

Doc: You're going to be hurt, child, worse than you've ever been hurt. Don't you know that boy's headed back for prison? Besides, if you two go into Lordsburg together, he's going to know all about you.

Dallas: He's not going into Lordsburg. All I want is for you to tell me it's all right.

Doc: Gosh, child, who am I to tell you what's right or wrong? All right, go ahead—do it if you can. Good—good luck.

Dallas: Thanks, Doc.

Doc: Ringo—

Curly: Well, Doc?

Doc: Both doing nicely. She's a real soldier's wife, that young lady.
Gatewood: Good—good. Then we can leave immediately.

Doc: Well, not for a day or so, if you want my professional advice.

Gatewood: What do you mean a day or so? Stay another day? Why?

Doc: Where were you when the stork came last night, Gatewood?

Hatfield: I refuse to let Mrs. Mallory travel until she and the child are out of danger.

Gatewood: What do you mean danger? Aren't we in worse danger here?

Peacock: I don't wish to intrude—but —I've had five children—I mean my dear wife has—and much as I dislike discussing it in this hour of our trial, I—I believe the doctor's right.

Doc: Spoken like a man, Reverend.
Gatewood: I say we ought to leave here before the Apaches find us. That's common sense.

Hatfield: I wish you were ten years younger, Gatewood.
Gatewood: Don't let my white hairs stop you.
Buck: Wait a minute, I . . .

Curly: Wait a minute . . .
Buck: Aw, Curly, I haven't said a word . . .
Curly: Now you shut up.

Curly: If we argue this thing out right we'll get somewhere. Let's all sit down and talk sensible. Come on, Buck—sit down.

Doc: There's a young woman in the kitchen making coffee
—she needs help.
Ringo: Thanks, Doc.

Doc: Say, Kid—how old were you when you went to the
pen?

Ringo: Oh, I was goin' on seventeen . . .

Ringo: Mornin', ma'am.
Dallas: Morning.

Ringo: I—laid awake most of the night—

Ringo: —wondering what you'da said if Curly hadn't busted in . . .

Ringo: Guess you was up kinda late, too—I heard you movin' around . . .

Ringo: You didn't answer what I asked you last night.

Dallas: Look, Kid, why don't you try to escape? There's a horse out there in the corral. Curly won't go after you because he can't leave the passengers in a fix like this.

Ringo: I got to go to Lordsburg. Why don't you go to my ranch and wait for me?

Dallas: Wait for a dead man? You haven't got a chance.

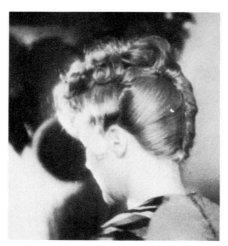

Dallas: It was three against one when the Plummers swore that you killed their foreman and got you sent up.

Dallas: It'll be three against one in Lordsburg.

Ringo: Well, there's some things a man just can't run away from.

Dallas: How can you talk about your life and my life when you're throwing 'em away? Yeah—mine, too! That's what you're throwing away if you go to Lordsburg!

Ringo: What do you want me to do?

Dallas: Would it make us any happier if Luke Plummer was dead? One of his brothers would be after you with a gun. We'd never be safe. I don't want that kind of life, Ringo.

Ringo: Well, I don't see what else I can do.

Dallas: Go now—get away—forget Lordsburg—forget the Plummers.

Dallas: Make for the border and I'll come to you.

Ringo: Do you mean that?
Dallas: Yes, I do.

153

Ringo: Will you go with me, Dallas?
Dallas: Oh, I can't leave Mrs. Mallory and the baby. I'll come to you from Lordsburg. I swear it.

Ringo: Well—I oughta have my rifle.

Dallas: I've got one—I got it here—I got it last night, while they were all asleep.

Ringo: You mean you thought of this last night?
Dallas: Yes—don't ask any more questions—not now!

Dallas: Go on—go on . . .

Buck: There ain't no Apaches behind us, Curly. We can still go back to Tonto.
Gatewood: No! I insist we go on to Lordsburg.

Curly: What do you think, Chris?

Chris: Geronimo between here and Lordsburg with my horse—I think.

Doc: *My horse—she has gone—*
She has gone astray—
With the sun . . .

Buck: Quiet, Doc. This is a serious matter, ain't it?

Doc: My dear Buck, if I have only one hour more to live, I'm going to enjoy myself.

Peacock: Doctor, I don't begrudge my samples, but I think . . .

Buck: Now you hush up! I've had enough out of you. We got a serious problem on our hands and nobody's talking any sense except me.

Curly: If we can get across that ferry, we'll be all right. Now, the question is what are we going to do about that lady and her baby . . .

Hatfield: Doctor Boone has settled that for us, suh, and I demand respect for his professional opinion.

Doc: Hatfield!

156

Curly: Ringo!

Curly: Ringo!

Curly: Ringo!

Dallas: Hurry, Ringo . . .

Curly: Ringo!
Dallas: Goodbye! . . .

Dallas: Ringo, don't stop! Go on—go on! Keep riding, Ringo . . . go on, go on . . .

Dallas: Curly, let him . . .

Ringo: You don't need them, Curly. I ain't going to run away.
Curly: I'll say you ain't.

Ringo: Look at them hills.

Curly: Apaches?
Ringo: Yeah—war signals.

Buck: Bridesmaid! Yow . . . yow . . .
Hey, Curly, why—don't you think you oughta take them cuffs off the kid? He's mighty handy with a gun.

Curly: You drive them hosses. I'll take care of the Kid.
Buck: Oh!

Gatewood: Can't you drive any faster? You stupid lout—we've got to make that ferry . . .

Gatewood: A man works all his life to get hold of some money so that he can enjoy life and then runs into a trap like this.

Peacock: Trap, Brother? You mean the Apaches? There's been no sign of them.
Gatewood: You don't see any signs of them. They strike like rattlesnakes . . .

Gatewood: If you hadn't insisted on waiting for her . . . we'd have been across the ferry by this time.

Hatfield: You talk too much, Gatewood.

Gatewood: Your threats don't faze me, Hatfield. You're nothing but a tinhorn gambler.
Hatfield: How would you like to get out and walk?
Gatewood: You can't put me out of a public conveyance!
Doc: Oh, now gentlemen—gentlemen . . .

Ringo: Take it easy, Gatewood . . . we may need that fight before we get to the Ferry.

Gatewood: You wouldn't be much good in a fight, you jailbird.

Hatfield: Oh, leave the Kid alone—he's handcuffed.

Peacock: Gentlemen, please, let's not forget the ladies, bless them—let us have a little Christian charity one for the other.

Curly: Well, folks, we're comin' into Lee's Ferry now . . .
Buck: Lordsburg, next stop.

Buck: Nice girl—get alang—get alang—

Buck: Curly, look! Look at the ferry—it's burned, too.

Curly: Hatfield, stand guard over there.

Gatewood: Where's the Army? Where's the soldiers?
Curly: Stay there, Doc.
Gatewood: Are they going to let Geronimo pillage and burn the whole country?

Curly: Will you give me your word you won't try to escape no more?
Ringo: I give you my word — to Lordsburg.

Curly: Get in the coach with them women?

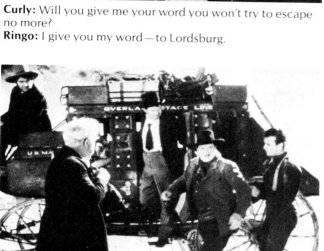

Ringo: I gave you my word.
Dallas: Ringo, don't.

Curly: Drive her into the river till she's up to the hubs.

Buck: Baby — Bridesmaid — Yow! . . .
Come on Baby, — whoa, girl — steady now . . .

Ringo: Look out, Curly . . .

Curly: Kid, take your suspenders and cross-tie them wheels . . .

Buck: Sorry about the saddle, Kid . . .
Curly: Ready, Kid? Ready, Buck? . . . Here we go . . . Just set tight, folks, and you'll be all right.

Ringo: Ya, ya!

Buck: Honey, chile . . . Steady—steady, Bridesmaid . . .
Buck: Come on, girl . . .
Buck: Easy now . . .

Ringo: Ya, ya!

Buck: Whoa, girl . . .

Buck: All aboard for Lordsburg— Lordsburg—

Buck: That's the girl. Take it easy!

Curly: Ya! Ya!

Buck: All aboard for Lordsburg—Lordsburg!

Buck: Say, Curly . . .
Curly: Yes?
Buck: Do you think I ought to charge Mrs. Mallory's baby half fare? . . .

Curly: Sweetheart!

Gatewood: Well, we'll soon be in Lordsburg. Well, sorry I flew off the handle, Hatfield. My apologies, Doctor. No hard feelings, I hope.

Peacock: All in all, it's been an exciting—a very interesting trip, has it not?—

Doc: Well, now that we're out of danger, Mr. . . .

Peacock: . . . Peacock.

Doc: . . . And ladies and gentlemen, since it's unlikely that we will be meeting again socially—I'd like to propose a toast . . .

Doc: Major, Gatewood, Ringo—

Doc: Your health.

Gatewood & Hatfield: Thanks—Thank you, sir.

Buck: Get on, girl . . .
Get on—get on—Yow—Yow—yow—yow—yow
yooow—yooooow—

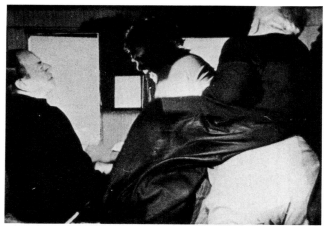

Gatewood: I warned you—I warned you of this danger—I told you not to wait for that woman . . . Let me out of here, I tell you . . .
Hatfield: Get back, you fool.

Buck: Yow—yow—yooooow—
Gatewood: We'll all be killed—we'll all be slaughtered!
Buck: Yow—yow—yow—yooow!
Doc: Gatewood, I've got a patient here—get back, you fool.

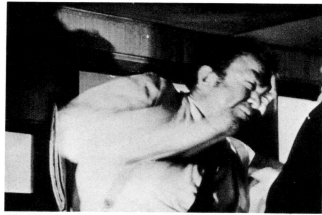

Gatewood: Take your hands off me, you drunken fool.

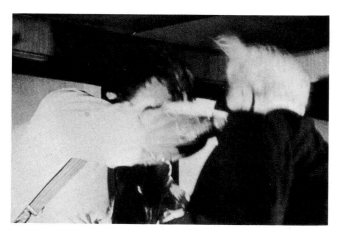

Curly: Get the leader . . .

Buck: Yow—yow—yow—yo—yo—YO!
Doc: Curly, more ammunition.

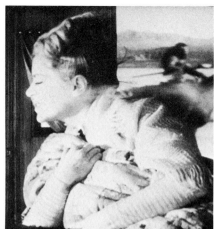

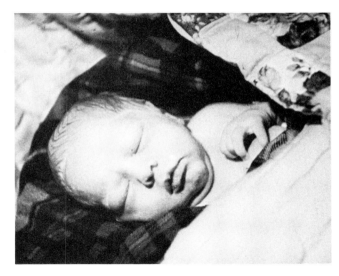
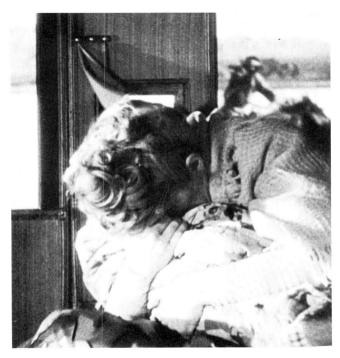

Lucy: Do you hear it? Do you hear it?
It's the bugle! They're blowing the charge!

202

Hatfield: If you see Judge Greenfield—tell him his son . . .

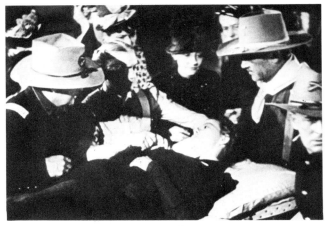

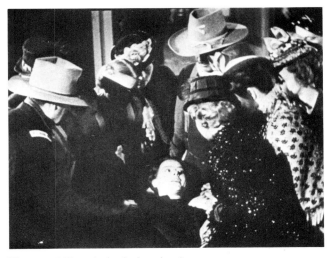

Captain: Thank heaven you're safe, Lucy.
Lucy: Where's Richard? Is he all right?
Captain: He's all right—don't you worry. It wasn't a bad wound. We'll take you to him immediately.

Woman: Where's the baby, dear?

Nurse: I'll take the baby.

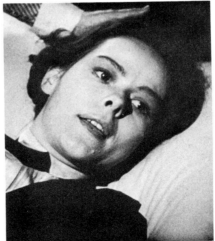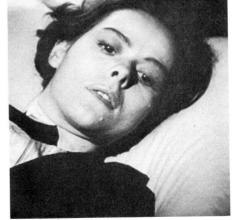

Lucy: Dallas, if there's ever anything I can do for . . .

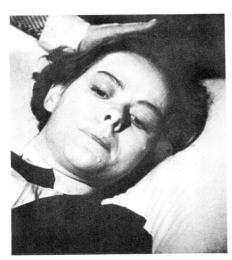  

Dallas: I know . . .

  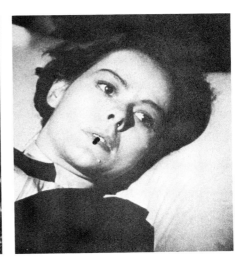

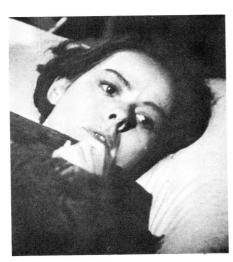  

Thin Man: It's the Ringo Kid!
Fat Man: Yeah—

Man: Aces and eights—dead man's hand, Luke.

Fat Man: Ringo Kid's in town.
Thin Man: Yeah—driving the stage.

Luke: *Mi hermano . . .*   **Spaniard:** Si—*patron . . .*

Luke: Cash in . . .

Soldier: Easy now . . .

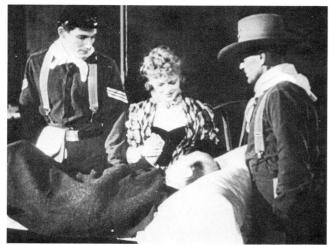

Peacock: Goodbye, Miss Dallas—if you ever come to Kansas City, Kansas, I want you to come out to see us.
Dallas: Well—thank you, Mr. . . .
Peacock: Peacock.

Curly: Well, Kid . . .

Ringo: Curly—how long will they give me for breakin' out?

Curly: Oh, about a year.

Ringo: You know where my ranch is?
Curly: Yeah.

Ringo: Will you see she gets there all right?
Curly: Dallas?

Ringo: Yeah. This is no town for a girl like her. Will you do it?
Curly: Sure.

Sheriff: Hiya, Marshal—get my man through all right?

218

Curly: I don't need 'em.

Gatewood: If you don't want to lose your man, sheriff, you'd better take him yourself.

Sheriff: What's your name, Mister?
Gatewood: My name is Gatewood—Ellsworth H. Gatewood.

Sheriff: Oh, Gatewood! You didn't think they'd get the telegraph wire fixed, did you?

Gatewood: You let me go—

Ringo: Can I meet you back here in ten minutes?
I gave you my word, Curly. I ain't goin' back on it now.

Curly: No ammunition.

Ringo: I lied to you, Curly—

Ringo: Got three left . . .

Ringo: Come on.

Dallas: Good night, Kid.

Ringo: Is this where you live?
Dallas: No!
Ringo: I got to know where you live, don't I?

Dallas: No—don't come any further. It's all been a crazy dream! I been out of my mind—just hoping. Say goodbye here, Kid.

Ringo: We ain't never gonna say goodbye.

Doc: Can I have that . . .

Luke: Give me the shotgun . . .   **Luke:** Shotgun!

Girl: Luke, Luke—please don't.

Dallas: Well, Kid, I—I told you not to follow me.

Ringo: Dallas! . . .

Ringo: I asked you to marry me, didn't I?

Dallas: I'll never forget you asked me, Kid.

Dallas: That's something.

Ringo: Wait here . . .

Buck: Whoa! . . .

Buck: Ringo said he'd be passing here in six or seven minutes.

Luke: Come on.

Doc: I'll take that shotgun, Luke.

Luke: You'll take it in the belly if you don't get out-a my way.

Doc: I'll have you indicted for murder if you step outside with that shotgun.

Luke: We'll attend to you later.

Doc: Don't ever let me do that again.

Woman: Luke . . .

Editor: Hey, Billy—hey, Billy—kill that story about the Republican convention in Chicago—

Editor: Billy, take this down instead . . . The Ringo Kid was killed on Main Street in Lordsburg tonight and . . .

Editor: among the additional dead were . . .

Editor: leave that blank for a spell.

Typesetter: I didn't hear no shooting, Ed.
Editor: You will, Billy, you will.

A Plummer: Missed him at four feet.

Dallas: Ringo—   **Dallas:** Ringo—   **Dallas:** Ringo . . .

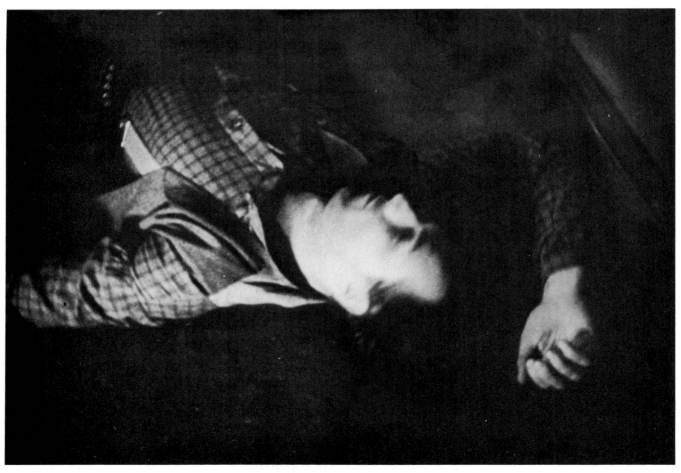

Curly: Ready, Kid?

Ringo: Thanks, Curly.

Ringo: Curly's going to see that you get to my place across the border. Well . . . goodbye, Dallas.

Dallas: Goodbye.

Curly: Maybe you'd like to ride aways with the Kid?
Dallas: Please.

Curly & Doc: Yow—yow—YOW—YOW . . .

Doc: Well, they're saved from the blessings of civilization.

Curly: Yeah—

Curly: Doc, I'll buy you a drink.

Doc: Just one.

CAST OF CHARACTERS

Dallas	CLAIRE TREVOR
Ringo Kid	JOHN WAYNE
Buck	ANDY DEVINE
Hatfield	JOHN CARRADINE
Doc Boone	THOMAS MITCHELL
Lucy Mallory	LOUISE PLATT
Curley	GEORGE BANCROFT
Peacock	DONALD MEEK
Gatewood	BERTON CHURCHILL
Lieutenant	TIM HOLT
Luke Plummer	TOM TYLER